When
The Eye is
Unobstructed

MINDFULNESS STORIES FOR AWAKENING

Francis Valloor

When
The Eye is
Unobstructed

MINDFULNESS STORIES FOR AWAKENING

Francis Valloor

ZEN
PUBLICATIONS
A DIVISION OF MAOLI MEDIA PRIVATE LIMITED

When the eye is unobstructed, the result is sight.
When the ear is unobstructed, the result is hearing.
When the mind is unobstructed, the result is truth.
And when the heart is unobstructed
the result is joy and love.

– Chuang Tzu, 4th Century BC

When The Eye is Unobstructed
Mindfulness Stories for Awakening

Many of the stories in this book were published earlier in *The Dewdrop in the Ocean*

Copyright © 2016 Francis Valloor

First Edition: 2017

Published by
ZEN PUBLICATIONS
A Division of Maoli Media Private Limited

60, Juhu Supreme Shopping Centre,
Gulmohar Cross Road No. 9, JVPD Scheme,
Juhu, Mumbai 400 049. India.

Tel: +91 9022208074
eMail: info@zenpublications.com
Website: www.zenpublications.com

Cover:
Detail from the work *'The Alpha Awakening Spring / Oil on Canvas'*
by Paul McCloskey
Author Photos: El Keegan
Book Design: Red Sky Designs, Mumbai

ISBN   978-93-85902-17-8

Printed by
Repro India Limited

All rights reserved. No part of this book may be reproduced or transmitted in any form or by any means, electronic or mechanical, including photocopying, recording, or by any information storage and retrieval system without written permission from the author or his agents, except for the inclusion of brief quotations in a review.

CONTENTS

Foreword

The simplest way to describe Awareness may be to liken it to seeing. To be aware is to be present so that your eyes are open and you can see. This way of seeing requires that we are present without judgements, that we see what is there, nothing else and nothing less.

This does not call for any training or practice. All that is asked of us, if we wish to see, is to remove the obstacles to seeing. Mystics and sages are men and women who see, and are able to show those who wish to see, how they may remove the obstacles before them.

The sage in these stories is not a single individual but someone who gives expression to the wisdom of the ages, men and women of East and West, of the past and the present. They are from different cultures and traditions such as the Hindu, Buddhist, Taoist, Christian, Sufi, and so on. You will hear in these stories the echoes of the Buddha, Ramana Maharshi, Anthony de Mello, Ramesh Balsekar, J. Krishnamurti, Meister Eckhart, Vernon Howard and many others.

The stories in this book as well as its companion volumes are based on various aspects of the single theme of Awareness/ Mindfulness. The ideas and insights contained here originate from humanity's great treasure of wisdom as well as the many teachers and experiences along my own life journey. All that I have done is to fashion these awareness stories in the way they are being presented, not unlike a craftsman who summons out of wood or metal some form for use or beauty.

These stories may inspire or infuriate, challenge or comfort, provoke or amuse. The purpose of parables and teaching stories is not to entertain or inform but to awaken and transform.

The message of Awareness is best learned through stories rather than rational discourse. Stories speak to you at a level beyond the mind without trying to change you or preach to you. They may bypass your resistance by not engaging the thinking mind and bring about a transformation that may open your eyes to see.

– Francis Valloor
Dublin

The Sage

Stories

The sage used stories as the most important medium of his teachings. He seemed to have an inexhaustible wealth of them which he enjoyed telling his listeners who would in turn be amused, intrigued, provoked and even shocked.

A scholar who was proud of his own erudition remarked, "I keep stories for my children at bed time. Why do you tell them to grown-ups?"

"You tell stories to children to put them to sleep," the sage replied. "I tell them to grown-ups to wake them up."

Secret

Many people were amazed at the peace and happiness
that the sage exuded. Yet he was no spiritual zombie but
embodied aliveness and vitality: efficient in his work with no sign
of stress in spite of the books he wrote, the lectures he gave and
the large number of people he constantly interacted with.

"What is the secret of your peace?" asked a visitor.

"Simple. I live and act with the conviction that it is not I who do
anything but Life acting through me and achieving its own
purpose. That leaves no room for personal striving or straining,
and no cause for pride or shame."

Doership

The sage's statement that he was never the doer of any action was incomprehensible to most people. So they would often come back with more questions.

"You say you are not the doer of actions," one of the visitors wondered. "Who then does the amazing things you do?"

"Life, Consciousness, God, call it what you will, but it is that," the sage replied.

"It's because you are special. That's not for ordinary mortals like me," the man said.

"Not so," the sage exclaimed. "The only difference between you and me is that I see and accept this totally, whereas you do not yet see it."

Listening

A first-time visitor asked the sage how he was supposed to listen. Was he to accept whatever the sage said like many gurus expected?

The sage replied, "I recommend an attitude of openness, not blind agreement. Neither blindly accept what I say nor reject it. Instead, listen critically and consider the truth of what you hear. And you'll benefit greatly if you can learn to listen to yourself in relation to what I say."

Ironies

One day the sage was in discussion with a group where he spoke freely about his own life journey.

Someone had a question for him: "What are some of the ironies that you have observed along the way?"

"Many indeed are the ironies of life but for me these stand out: teachers who can't learn, healers who are sick, religious people who hate, and holy people who can't laugh."

Serenity

The sage was an open book to some and a mystery to others who saw him as a rebel. However, they agreed that he was a "happy rebel", or a "rebel with a smile." Always pleasant and friendly with people who disagreed with him or branded him a heretic or troublemaker, he was incapable of harbouring rancour or resentment against them.

"You have rebelled against your religion, society and public opinion," one of the visitors protested. "And yet you never appear to be in conflict with anyone."

"I live by the light within," the sage replied. "I don't rebel or fight, oppose or preach. I'm only singing my song."

Silence

A visitor asked the sage how anyone could hope to understand the message of a sage.

The sage replied, "Silence is the best way to understand a sage. Words and concepts are of the mind. Useful, but not enough, and they are often obstacles."

"But that's not an easy way for most human beings," the visitor protested.

"Stories are the next best," the sage added.

Journey

Many people knew the sage as a mystic who had had some extraordinary spiritual experiences. While he would not deny those experiences, he would advise people not to seek them but to focus on their daily living.

One day a visitor asked, "Were there any stages in your spiritual journey?"

"Yes," he answered. "In the first stage I lived an ordinary everyday life. A second and very brief period involved some life-changing experiences. In the third, I'm back in the common daily life."

Pedestals

A man whose life had been deeply transformed after listening to the sage wondered why people did not listen to him in greater numbers.

"Building monuments to sages is a lot easier than listening to them," remarked the sage wryly. "It's easier to keep them on pedestals than to bring their message into life."

Paths

Someone asked the sage what lineage he belonged to, or whom he followed on the spiritual path.

"Paths are made by walking," the sage said rejecting the suggestion. "I follow no one and I seek no followers."

Ordinariness

To all appearances the sage was quite ordinary and he was content to be seen that way.

"What is the difference between an ordinary man and a sage?" someone asked the sage.

This was the sage's reply: "When an ordinary man attains awareness, he becomes a sage. When the sage attains awareness, he becomes an ordinary man."

Contradictions

To many observers and visitors the sage's life was a
mystery and some felt, full of contradictions. He loved
people while being independent. He was comfortable in the
company of others while valuing his time in solitude. He enjoyed
life while being strangely detached from material things.

When a new group of visitors criticised the sage's unpopular
stance in support of immigrants, a close friend observed, "It isn't
easy to understand someone whose foundation is hidden, whose
sustenance is unseen and whose movement resembles stillness."

Escape

The sage's talks about spiritual realities, like God, inner quest and enlightenment, drew large crowds who listened to him eagerly as they felt those discourses were truly uplifting.

However, when he shifted his emphasis to daily living in awareness, many were disappointed.

When asked about the change, the sage explained, "For most people spirituality is an escape from daily life. When it helps people bring heaven to earth, it's of value but many prefer to live with their feet firmly planted in the clouds."

Inspiration

Inspired by the teachings of her religion, a social worker devoted her life to working for the poor. As a recipient of several awards and recognitions, she was an icon of service.

In her conversation with the sage she praised him, "I heard recently that you help many poor people in this town. That has inspired many people."

"I haven't done anything to inspire anyone, and they were not my actions," the sage told her. "I'm only an instrument through which actions were done. So I take no credit for them."

"And you're so humble! I find that truly inspiring!" she exclaimed. "I'm neither humble nor proud, I'm aware."

Receptivity

The sage was in great demand as a speaker in many countries. His listeners readily acknowledged the wisdom of his teachings.

An interviewer once asked the sage if his teachings had always been well received.

"Far from it," the sage said. "At first they were the object of derision, then they were violently opposed. Now they are seen to be quite obvious!"

Advice

The sage would answer all the questions that people asked him but would not offer them unsolicited advice. Having given spontaneous advice in response to a specific request, he would not insist that it be followed.

One day the discussion was on parenting, and knowing that the sage's children had grown well into their own lives, a visitor asked him what the secret was.

"Well, I never offered any advice to my children because my counsel would be at least one generation too old for them," the sage answered.

As the questioner took in those words, he continued. "And when sometimes I did, they were smart enough to ignore my advice."

Harmony

A group of scientists were in dialogue with the sage. During a discussion, one of them asked, "What is the challenge to human consciousness from science, technology and communication?"

"The need for balance between the inner and the outer," was the sage's immediate reply.

Asked for an explanation, he continued, "When you're able to explore the inner space as ceaselessly and daringly as you have done in your adventures in the outer world, you will have brought balance into life." After a pause he added, "And you will have discovered fire once again."

Treasures

One of his visitors told the sage that contact with him had turned his life upside down. "I had come to dip my toes in the water but now I am in deep waters."

"If it's safety you wanted you would have stayed on shore," commented the sage. "But the security of the land would have been a prison for your spirit."

"I see that now," conceded the visitor. "Yet the fear persists."

"Great treasures," said the sage, "are found in the depths of the ocean. My job is to help you take the plunge. And look at the irony! Your fear is of your own depth and the vastness of the treasures within!"

Imitation

The sage described how his moment of awakening happened when he was walking by the bank of a nearby river.

Thereafter, many of his listeners were at the river walking mindfully hoping for a similar experience. When the sage heard this, he was greatly amused.

"Awakening is not something you can bring on by matching the externals or imitating someone else's actions," he admonished gently. "It's never attained by practice, nor is it a reward for good conduct. It just comes to you unbidden."

Wisdom

Those who knew the sage closely regarded him as an astute observer of human nature. To many others, the sage's simplicity, trust and lack of judgment of people appeared naïve and childlike.

"When I'm with people," he would explain, "I don't feel the need to make a forced choice between the good and the bad. Being open and receptive is more effective than trying to change them."

"Don't you see that some of these people are in fact lying and hoodwinking you?"

"That may be so," he conceded. "But I also see that people tend to be good and truthful when they are accepted with goodness and trust."

Effectiveness

A television interviewer emphasised how wonderful it was to witness the eagerness of people to see the sage. "In fact, most of them keep coming back to your talks and workshops."

"It is certainly true that they want to see me and hear me again and again," the sage said. "My work is effective when they wake up to discover in themselves what they're finding in me."

Insomnia

After listening to the sage's talks a few times, a man said with regret, "I think I have given this a good shot, but I am afraid I am in the wrong place because when the sage speaks I just fall asleep."

"In my case he had the opposite effect," one of the listeners responded.

"How is that?" the man asked.

"When I started listening to the sage, I couldn't sleep even in the night," he replied. "That was when I began to wake up!"

Saints

One day the discussion turned to the follies of saints. Some thought saints were those who were flawless enough to have stopped making mistakes. They would be marked by perfection, unlike sinners who erred and offended.

"Plaster of Paris saints may be perfect, never the living ones," the sage declared. "When you know saints and sinners well enough, it's hard to tell the difference."

As the group considered that comment, he added with a smile, "And if you really want to know about saints and sages, ask their spouses."

Values

A retired government official said that he had lived by his values and religious teachings. "That is what has brought me peace of mind and respect of people," he added.

"That is the way for many people," the sage said. "As for me I find it easier to be led by awareness."

"How does that work out in practical life?"

"I eat not to stay alive or because it is time to eat, but because I'm hungry," the sage answered. "I don't help someone because I am enjoined by religious teachings or higher values, but because they need help."

Awareness

Seeing

A philosopher once asked the sage, "Can you sum up all your teaching in one sentence?"

"Why, I can sum up all my teaching, in fact, all of life in one word," the sage replied.

"What's that word?"

"Seeing."

Projections

The sage was once asked, "What is the essence of awareness?"

"Seeing whatever is there and not something else."

"But isn't that what everyone sees?"

"Far from it!" explained the sage "An astronaut gazes at the moon and sees a destination. Looking at the same moon, the hungry man sees an omelette and a lover the face of his beloved."

Defensiveness

A woman who attended one of the sage's retreats left after the first day. The theme of the day was facing the truth of one's life. She left behind a message that stated the reason for her early departure: "I am sorry, this is too personal. I can't take it."

One of the participants commented that it was a snub.

The sage, however, saw it differently. "This is, in fact, a compliment," he noted. "Truths are beautiful as long as they are kept lofty and distant and not allowed to come close enough to upset people. Most people are looking for amusement, not awareness."

Dreams

A successful entrepreneur and head of a large philanthropic organisation said, "I have many dreams I'd like to realise in this life. I would love to do whatever I can to change the world and alleviate suffering in some way. Please advise me, what is the best thing for me to do?"

Without a moment's hesitation came the sage's reply: "The best thing would be to wake up."

Explanation

A visiting philosopher expressed his confusion to the sage, "People's behaviour has always baffled me – how they sabotage their own goals, how they destroy the lives of the people they love and how they fight in the name of peace."

"When you acknowledge that humanity is mostly asleep and unaware, most mysteries about human beings are resolved and human nature is then quite readily understood," the sage replied.

Process

"I realise what you're teaching is important for me but I'm hardly in the present," a professor admitted. "When I'm not regretting or reminiscing the past, I'm worrying about the future."

"Awareness is the understanding of how everything works or how life unfolds," the sage responded. "It's when you don't see the process behind all things that you get stuck in the past and caught up in the future."

Learning

A retired civil servant was in discussion with the sage about his family and his relationship with his children.

"Sound travels much slower than light I can assure you. Some of the things I told my children when they were teenagers reached them only twenty years later," he commented.

The sage nodded in agreement. "Why, some of the things I tell people reach them decades later. If indeed, they get there at all."

Expansion

One of the visitors asked, "How is it, that in the same circumstances of life, some people live a constricted existence limited mostly to their work and family, while others enjoy far richer, expansive lives?"

"Birds fly in freedom because their wings make it possible. Fish thrive in the ocean because they can swim," the sage replied. "Life shrinks or expands in proportion to your awareness."

Inquiry

A visitor who was greatly exercised over the impact of the sage's teachings, spoke up, "I don't think what you teach is good for us. They are dangerous and quite contrary to what our society has instilled in us."

"The first question to ask of any reality is not whether it's good or bad, for that is a judgment that blocks all inquiry," the sage responded calmly. "Instead, let the first question be: is it true or false?"

Sleepwalking

"A businessman complained, "I have lived a good life. I have worked hard, maintained my relationships, though I'd my fair share of scraps. I even started a spiritual practice a few years ago but I'm still not at peace."

"I'm reminded of a long distance driver who, upon hearing unusual engine sounds, turned up the music," the sage replied. "He disabled the annoying indicator lights that flashed. A little later, stranded on the highway, he wondered why his treasured car would so let him down."

As some of the listeners asked for an explanation, the sage continued, "Most of us are sleepwalking through life. So we hardly observe what is going on around us or even within us. And then we wonder why we are so unhappy."

Phantoms

A visitor was upset about how he always seemed to be living in the past feeling guilty or ashamed, or in the future contemplating things that hardly ever came true. "It is as if I am always running away from the phantoms of my past and future."

"Phantoms indeed," the sage agreed. "Reality is never a problem. The trouble is the mind. It creates images and judgements and you demand that things be different from the way they are."

Now

A well-read man said he had attended numerous retreats but was frustrated that for all his efforts he was unable to live in the moment.

"Please teach me how I can practise living in the Now," he begged.

"If you need to practise, you haven't understood because awareness cannot be practised, it is simply lived," the sage said. "Nor can you relate the Now moment to the past or future. For when you compare it is no longer the Now."

Reflection

"Before I came to see you I was quite happy, but after listening to you, so much muck has been stirred up inside. I feel depressed," a listener moaned.

"Awareness shines on the pleasant and the unpleasant alike," the sage replied. "If you stop stirring it even more with your judgements, the muck will settle and the water will be clear again."

Vision

An elderly man said he had been on a world cruise with a friend. They had visited several new countries, stayed in fabulous places and enjoyed breath-taking sceneries.

"New places and situations do stimulate the mind," he noted. "So I consider it a great voyage, a journey of self-discovery."

"For a true voyage of discovery, what is needed are not new landscapes and sceneries but new eyes to see," commented the sage.

Resistance

"How is it that many people react with anger and resistance to the message of sages?" a visitor asked.

"When you're in deep sleep and someone attempts to wake you up, you're likely to be annoyed," the sage answered.

"Many people, after years of contact with you, still seem to have such difficulty understanding you," the visitor said.

"When people's comfort and security depend on not understanding, they won't," the sage explained.

Confirmation

The sage would sometimes say that what most seekers are interested in is only confirmation, not challenges. One day he told them this version of an Aesop Fable.

"A hunter asked a wood cutter if he had seen any lion tracks in the area. 'If you want, I can lead you right to the lion himself,' replied the wood cutter. The hunter stopped in his tracks and stammered, 'No…no… not the lion… It's… just the footprints I'm looking for.'"

The sage then commented: "People are settling for the least. They don't want to see the lion, only the tracks; they don't want the experience, only the belief. They wish to know they are heading in the right direction, and feel reassured, not challenged."

Peace

A visitor, distressed by many painful life events, was searching for peace. He had tried religion, meditation and psychotherapy, but none of those had helped. He wanted to get away from it all and be at peace.

"Your conflict is between what is and what is not," the sage explained to him. "You are trying to find peace by escaping what is, but that never works."

"What can I do to end this conflict?" the visitor asked.

"There is only one way you can do that," the sage answered. "You can find peace only by coming to terms with reality. Steadfastly refuse to look away from what you see."

Repetitions

A woman told the sage that her husband and she had visited a small town in Southern France on vacation every summer for the past twenty-one years.

"Wow!" exclaimed one of the other visitors, "That is twenty-one visits, each giving so many rich experiences."

"It may also be one experience repeated twenty-one times," the sage commented. "And that for most people is life in a nutshell."

Reality

A young man was shocked that his father had told a lie. "Other people may tell lies, but not my father. That's what I had thought until now."

"Seeing reality has shattered an illusion, but you see how much you grow up when you see your father as another human being, sometimes honest, sometimes dishonest," the sage suggested.

Speaking to the others present, he continued, "People prefer illusions, not reality. Some people even think their parents never had sex."

Truth

The sons of a businessman found out that their trusted family friend and business partner was cheating their father out of money. The young men chose to follow their uncle's advice, "Don't tell dad, his ulcers will flare."

One of the sons approached the sage for counsel and was told, "There is no experience more growth-promoting than confrontation with the truth. It may hurt, but it always heals."

Realism

A middle-aged man said he had passed through many difficulties in life. "I had started off as a man with visions and dreams but reality knocked them out of me," he said. "So I decided to jettison my dreams and become more realistic about life."

"Reality wakes you up but realism kills your dreams and visions," the sage said. "Reality sets you free, it's realism that has hobbled you."

Conditioning

Commitment

The morning news reported a major suicide attack that killed scores of people.

"Whatever you may say, you have to admire their readiness to die for a cause," commented one visitor.

"Does that make it right for them to kill people?" asked another.

"They are choosing to give up their lives for a cause. We have to admire their courage and commitment even if we don't agree with them," continued the former.

"Neither justify nor blame, for they, like others, have no choice in the matter," said the sage. "They are thoroughly programmed."

Prejudice

"Most people don't see anything as it is," the sage observed. "They have their prejudices and fixed ideas and they compulsively take sides. This distorts and colours their perceptions."

To illustrate this, he told his listeners a story. A man who survived a shipwreck was washed ashore on an island. When he came to, he found himself surrounded by strange-looking islanders in a totally unfamiliar environment.

"Is there a government on this island?" asked the man.

"Yes there is," the islanders told him helpfully.

"Well," declared our man, "I'm against it."

Ideology

A psychologist spoke on the influence of nature and nurture on human beings. "Our development and behaviours are programmed by our genes and conditioning," he explained. "These two factors set the limits of our growth, development and behaviours."

The sage nodded in agreement. A philosopher in the group was not pleased, "Isn't that too restrictive? What about human freedom?"

"But we have to be faithful to the ideal of human freedom," the philosopher insisted.

"You will see this clearly," the sage added, "if your faithfulness is to the reality of life and not to some theory of freedom."

Modifications

"Are sages free from conditioning? Does enlightenment spell its end?" asked a visitor.

"Far from it," the sage replied. "Look at the way they dress, their eating habits, languages, accents and so on. Such conditioning may be modified, but they don't disappear."

"If they are conditioned like everyone else, what is the difference?"

"The difference," explained the sage, "is that their understanding transforms them, so they do not react but respond to people and situations. Since they know who they are, they cannot see themselves as separate from others. When the eyes see only one reality, the heart is undivided, and conditioning no longer holds sway over them."

Belonging

It was the country's day of independence and a celebration of nationalism. For the sage, nationality was an artificial label and nationalism a dangerous conditioning.

"But nationality gives us a sense of belonging, doesn't it?" asked a disciple.

"This sense of belonging is an artificial device imparted through conditioning to keep you bound to the herd," the sage said. "Being part of 'Us' may make you feel good, but it may also make you hostile to those you consider part of 'Them'."

Nationalism

The sage took no part in patriotic demonstrations. To the dismay of some of his friends who were in politics, he would not go out of his way to honour the national flag nor would he dishonour it.

He considered nationalism, along with religion, a great divider of humanity.

Once when he was asked to explain his position, he remarked, "A sage is free from the conditioning called nationalism. Inwardly, he belongs nowhere so that he can be everywhere and love everyone."

Survival

A serving military officer on vacation confessed that in obeying an unjust order he had killed several innocent and unarmed civilians in a reprisal raid. He had known it was a terribly wrong thing to do.

"There is little I can do in such a situation. I must live!" the officer said.

The sage looked at him steadily and asked, "Must you?"

Scarcity

A wealthy man described how he had witnessed appalling poverty and squalor on his frequent travels abroad. He wished to alleviate it in some way.

He had grown up in times of serious financial problems in the country and suffered poverty at home and was "forced to take every penny a prisoner."

"Even though that was my story and now I live in abundance, I must say I'm reluctant to donate money for fear I may not have enough for the future," he said.

"Your scarcity mentality and compulsion to save are habits and attitudes that have outlived their purpose," the sage said. "Saving was necessary at one time but now presents as hoarding."

Victims

There was a suicide terrorist attack in the national capital in which there were heavy casualties. Some of the visitors informed the sage that the government had announced generous monetary compensations for the families of the victims.

"Have they included the suicide bombers in the category of the victims?" asked the sage to the shock and disbelief of the listeners.

Proxy

"Most people do not live their own lives but those of society, their parents or others. A most important question every person should ask is, 'Whose life am I living?'" suggested the sage.

"How do I find out?" a visitor asked.

"A good place to start is to listen to yourself in critical times," the sage answered. "When you are angry, disappointed or under stress, what do you say or do? Whose words, what tone of voice, what gestures do you use?"

Support

A woman said that she had always needed someone strong in her life. "Alone, I feel lost and helpless," she said.

"When you were a child and were afraid, you cried. You ran away and clung to someone bigger than you. Then, your reaction protected you, now it restricts you," the sage told her. "You're like most human beings who repeat the same answers to questions that have long since changed."

Programming

A man said he was mild mannered like his own father. Like him, he would also ignore many unpleasant situations and then flare up at some minor provocation.

"I was shocked to hear myself scream at my six-year-old son. I used the same words and emphasis as my father did!" he noted.

"You learn much about yourself from your reactions to conflicts and crises," the sage responded.

"Please tell me, am I bound to remain so?" the father asked.

"Of course not," said the sage, "as you wake up and understand your programming, you're setting yourself free."

Oxymoron

A young scholar said he had completed his doctoral studies in Christian Spirituality. Before he set out to teach the subject, he was visiting the sage to draw some inspiration from him.

The sage, who drew a clear distinction between spirituality and religion, asked, "Is Christian Spirituality not a contradiction in terms? As I see it, you can speak of Christian conditioning but not Christian Spirituality."

The young scholar suggested that it was too sharp and arbitrary a distinction to make and sought to understand the sage's perspective.

"Real spirituality cannot be Christian, Hindu or Buddhist; it is the space beyond such conditioning," the sage explained. "The function of spirituality is to set you free to come to this."

Predicament

Is conditioning invariably harmful?" asked a visitor.

"No. Conditioning gives answers, brings some regularity into life. It makes living easier in many situations."

"When is it harmful, then?"

The sage explained further, "When your conditioning gives ready made answers whereas growth is in finding your own; when it brings predictability instead of change; when it protects you from life instead of launching you out to explore; when you have fixed responses to changing life situations; when it keeps you stuck instead of setting you free."

Accents

"Our conditioning often functions like a glass through which we look, without, in fact, seeing it," said the sage. "We notice the limitations of our conditioning when we are faced with difficult situations that become like mirrors that reflect us. Otherwise we are unaware of them."

A young American visitor agreed with the sage and added that he had learned this on his recent trip to Australia. When some Australians had complained that they had difficulty understanding his accent, he had replied, "It's not me who pronounces words strangely. It's you who have an accent."

Judgements

Disturbance

A man complained that the sound of television and loud music from his neighbour's apartment often kept him awake in the night.

"I feel angry. And I blame him, the police, the government, everybody for this," he concluded.

"The sound and fury of your inner tirades may be louder than the blaring of music. That will keep you awake even after the outside sounds have settled down," the sage suggested. "Besides, isn't it more intelligent to take appropriate action than being angry?"

The man returned later to tell the sage that, by letting go of his judgements, he now slept peacefully, even when disturbing noises could be heard outside.

Degeneration

An old man said he was upset about the ways of the young. "Their moral sense is abominable. Respect for older people is a thing of the past. There is no consideration for other people."

"Do you think this is new? How was it in your day?" the sage asked.

"Well, in my youth we were far more respectful. We obeyed our elders."

"Let me read something that may be of some comfort to you," the sage began.

Then, from a piece of paper, he read: 'Our earth is degenerate in these latter days; bribery and corruption are common; children no longer obey their parents; and the end of the world is evidently approaching.'

"When do you think this was written?" he asked

"That sounds quite contemporary."

"Well, this is from an Assyrian clay tablet dated 2800 BC," the sage told the old man.

"Passage of time offers no guarantee of change in such matters."

Choices

A friend talked about her tendency to judge people. "Your judgments imply that others are responsible for the way they think, feel and behave," stated the sage.

"Are you implying that people aren't responsible?" she asked.

"People are the way they are because of their conditioning and genetic factors," replied the sage. "Nobody chooses to be ugly, tight-fisted, hot tempered, obese, thin, needy, unfaithful, selfish, or cruel. It is futile to blame them."

"People do make choices, don't they?" she persisted.

"Of course," said the sage, "or so it appears."

Standards

"People apply different standards to themselves and others," a friend observed.

"That's so true!" exclaimed the sage. "People would like to be accepted for how they are but their judgements of others are based on how they ought to be."

Inclusion

"A person who is awake and aware does not judge another human being," stated the sage. "Prostitutes and tax collectors were comfortable with Jesus because they felt accepted."

"How was that possible?" one of the visitors asked.

"Because he didn't think he was better than them. So there was no ground for judging any of them," answered the sage.

Self-Healing

"I see how judgmental I've been towards my husband," a woman reproached herself. "Though I see this, I don't know how to stop it."

"Judgements of others are the echoes of self-hate. Look for qualities that you hate in other people. You'll see what you need to heal in yourself," suggested the sage. "When you stop judging others for these, you've healed them in yourself."

Blameless

A visitor confessed that he was overly critical of other
people. He had tried to change but had not succeeded. Would the
sage share with him what had helped him in his own life?

The sage replied that what had helped him was the realisation
that it is the same God or Consciousness that was working
through everyone. "So you and I are not individual actors,
independently choosing to do whatever we wish to."

As the questioner tried to understand this simple response, the
sage continued, "I could no longer judge the actions of people
as faults, mistakes, failings or sins and blame them. In fact, I
couldn't even judge myself."

Humour

A group of religious leaders were in discussion with the sage. Asked if he had any advice for them, the sage replied mischievously, "I would heartily recommend a sense of humour – and a measure of sensuality. I think if religious leaders laughed enough and enjoyed life a little more, they would be less moralising and judgmental of others."

Some of them nodded in agreement while others appeared uncomfortable. "But we teach what God has appointed us to teach, nothing more," protested one of them.

"How is it that when you take religion too seriously, so does your God?" the sage wondered. "God becomes judgemental, he loses his sense of humour, becomes hot-tempered and starts nit-picking."

After a pause he continued, "And, by the way, why is God so preoccupied with sex?"

Intimacy

Judgements are the biggest obstacle in relationships," the sage told his audience. "You can't love what you judge and seek to control."

"Does that mean we can't love another person if we have judgements about them?" a visitor asked.

"Judgements limit your ability to see people with clarity," the sage replied. "Intimacy is seeing another person without judgements."

Barriers

A seeker admitted that he was frustrated and angry with himself for his many failures. He felt these were setbacks and barriers on his journey towards God.

"Every time you judge yourself, you're creating a barrier," the sage told him.

"How is that?"

"Because you believe that there is a journey to be made which is not the case," the sage said, "and because you think self-criticism begins and ends with yourself and does not involve a rejection of the one who lives and works through you."

Expectations

A woman said she had realised that, while on the surface her relationship with her husband was smooth, she was a cauldron of seething judgements. "I'm bothered by his thoughtlessness, his coming home late, the way he talks. I wish I weren't doing this."

"Convert your judgements into statements of expectations and see what you are not getting from him," the sage recommended. "See also the role of your fears in the judgements you make. You wouldn't judge if you weren't fearful."

Evidence

A businessman said he and his partner had managed their business without any difficulty. Lately he has been convinced that the man was secretive and withdrawn. "I'm sure he has his hands in the till. It's only a matter of time and I'll find enough evidence to support this."

"When there is a will to condemn, evidence is not far behind," was the sage's response.

Interference

The sage had little patience with religious and moral crusaders.

When questioned about this, he explained, "Those are the people who not only renounce the ordinary pleasures of life but find great satisfaction in denying those pleasures to other people."

Perspective

"There are two ways of relating to people," the sage said to a visitor. "You can see yourself as a victim of what they do to you. Then you're fearful, judgemental and powerless."

"What is the other way?"

"You can see with wakeful eyes," the sage replied. "Then the angry person looks scared. The snobbish person looks shy. The controlling person looks anxious. Your perception of them is replaced by true seeing. You may be surprised at who comes across as the victim then. The idea that they are doing something to you is replaced by your vision of them."

Original

"Use your judgements as a mirror to see your own reflection," the sage suggested.

"I am quite demanding and strict with myself," the headmaster of a school said. "But towards my teachers and students I'm unfailingly kind. I certainly don't judge them harshly."

"Or so it may seem," the sage told him with a smile. "If you don't judge yourself, you won't judge anyone else either. If you are harsh with yourself, so are you with others. For when you send out a message, in some way the original always stays with you."

Ingratitude

A social worker who had spent many years working for her local community said, "I've gone out of my way to help people but I find no gratitude. There is little more than selfishness in people."

The sage's comment was, "Where judgements end, happiness begins."

Oneness

A man who had listened to the sage was acutely aware of the many judgements that he made of himself and other people.

"I'm fed up with myself for all the judgements I make constantly. Will I ever stop them?" he wanted to know.

"Your judgements will reduce when you see that they arise from the sense of separation and division you experience," the sage replied. "Judgements end when you experience the oneness of all reality, when you realise that you are one with all there is."

Shadow

Awakening

A young man said he was fed up with the materialism and godlessness in his country and was setting out to the East in search of spirituality and God.

"The moment of awakening is seeing that what you are seeking is to be found neither in the East nor in the West, but in the centre of your own being," the sage suggested. "You can see it now or you can see it when you return home from the East."

Completion

An elderly man, who had a reputation for his intense
spiritual practices, austere life and teaching against sexuality,
was arrested for sexual misconduct. Some people were upset and
disappointed. Others had their faith shaken. Others still were
angry.

The sage refused to join the chorus of condemnation against him.

He said, "Take care not to pursue holiness by fighting your life
energy and its impulses."

When asked to clarify, he added, "Life looks for completion;
it always fills in what has been left out, and what has not
been expressed in life-affirming ways, reappears as sins and
transgressions."

Recognition

Some of the visitors expressed shock at the reports of cruelty and torture by police and military in a neighbouring country. One of them was convinced that it would never happen in his own country because its citizens had an ingrained sense of freedom and human dignity.

"All those noble ideas disappear when the unacknowledged side of human beings surfaces, and no one is exempt from this," the sage warned.

"Aren't the moral and religious people free from that?" someone asked.

"Far from it," the sage disagreed. "It is not necessarily the righteous and moral people, but happy people who refrain from cruelty against others."

Self-Discovery

The sage often said that the vast majority of human beings knew themselves very little and understood themselves even less. All our work of self-discovery was to bring to light what was hidden from view.

A listener asked, "Is there any path that can take us there?"

"Paths are many but the way is one. And that is awareness," the sage replied.

Polarities

Television and newspapers were full of news about a well-known and revered religious leader who had been sentenced to life imprisonment for rape and murder. Followers were shocked and others outraged. "How could he, a holy man, do such a thing?" they asked.

The sage was calm. "Pursuit of holiness is a dangerous occupation. Righteousness spawns hypocrisy. Morality engenders immorality," the sage told the astonished group. "When you pursue one, its opposite follows too. When you cultivate one, the other goes into hiding and becomes your foe."

Asked for an explanation, he asked, "Who is a devil but a god who hasn't been recognised?"

Eradication

A religious preacher urged followers to eradicate all evil tendencies in themselves. "Holiness and sin can't go together," he said. "Pay attention to every desire, mistake and attachment and remove them. That's the way to perfection."

When one of the preacher's followers sought the sage's counsel, he explained that chaff and wheat always occur together. "You can't cultivate one by destroying its opposite. You'll never find perfection through self-hate."

Masquerade

A group of holy men had vandalised a shrine of another religion. One of the visitors expressed how he was shocked every time he heard of virtuous and holy people showing such a vicious side to them.

The sage replied that he was not surprised as it was consistent with human nature.

"Selective cultivation of desirable virtues leads to the suppression of vices. So, I don't take people's virtuous side at face value," he explained. "In any case, most people's holiness is only fear masquerading as virtue and their non-violence the suppression of hatred and violence."

Breakthrough

A corporate lawyer, through brilliance and hard work, had become wealthy and well known. But happiness eluded him. A major financial reversal led to a prolonged depression. He sought the sage's counsel.

The sage told him a story from the Arabian Nights. "A farmer's plough gets caught in a powerful obstacle and breaks. He thinks he is ruined, but when he digs to remove the offending obstacle, he finds a large iron ring that has caught the plough. As he digs around it further, he finds that the ring is attached to the lid of a trunk. He pulls it out to find a treasure that has been buried there for a long time. He is now a very wealthy man." And the sage concluded the story with a smile, "Where you stumble, there you will discover your treasure."

The lawyer took the sage's story to heart. Later he would describe the encounter. "The sage gave me a spade and said, 'Dig!' And that is what brought me happiness at last."

Revelation

A large number of people had gathered for the sage's talk one day. To them he read this story, which had appeared in the newspapers.

"An old clay Buddha statue was being moved from its old site to its present location in the Wat Trainmit temple in Bangkok in 1957. The statue fell off the crane and sustained a crack. Further work was suspended until the following day. An anxious monk, who came in the night to check on the damage, shone a torch on the crack and found to his surprise that light reflected back from the cracked area. A little chipping of the mud revealed that the Buddha was made of pure gold but covered in hard clay. It weighed over 5 tons. The 700-year old Buddha had been covered in mud to hide it from the marauding Burmese army a few centuries earlier and nobody seemed to remember that the strong clay was only the exterior and concealed something precious."

He put the paper down and continued, "This is the truth about you. Within the clay exterior is the golden Buddha. That is who you are."

Patterns

A woman who was working at her fourth post in a bank declared she was fed up with her boss. Now she was making a special request for transfer to a fifth post which was likely to be granted because of her high level of competence.

When asked about her manager, she replied, "He is rude, insensitive, domineering and arrogant."

"How was the previous manager?" the sage asked.

"Well, he too was domineering, rude, arrogant and insensitive," she replied as before.

"If you want to work anywhere, the place to start is within yourself," counselled the sage. "If you don't, the next manager will be waiting for you with the same problems."

Disguise

A man who described himself as a surveyor turned spiritual seeker said, "This may sound like a conspiracy of life but my efforts at living a spiritual life have been thwarted at every turn by my own cravings and attachments. I look at the monks in the monastery I visit sometimes and wish my life were pure and trouble-free like theirs."

"What you avoid pursues you, what you deny affirms itself. We see ourselves in many disguises on the path of life," the sage replied. "What we long for in others and what we despise in others are lessons for us in self-understanding and freedom."

Illusions

The principal of a prestigious school was proud how she had mastered her job in one year. She said the teachers were in awe of her and unlike any of her predecessors, she had a great rapport with the parents.

It had come as a major shock when the teachers had gone on a flash strike against her 'high handedness'. "She never listens to us. She always has her way and her way is always harsh," they had complained.

When she met the sage, she was confused, "I don't know what went wrong."

"The ending of false ideas about yourself is a good preparation for finding out the truth about yourself," was the sage's challenge to her.

Heroism

There were widespread protests when a national hero was criticised in the media.

When asked what he thought about the hero's angry reactions, the sage responded, "Facing criticism is a sure benchmark of a person's growth. A true hero faces criticisms squarely and looks for the truth in the censure."

"Isn't it difficult for anyone to deal with criticism with equanimity?" asked one of the listeners.

"That's why true heroes are so rare," the sage agreed. "The biggest heroism is in the adventure of self-discovery and the readiness to face the truth about oneself."

Clay Feet

The sage taught that when people looked up to heroes and celebrities they risked denying their own power and dimming their own light.

"I've been disillusioned with most of the heroes in my life," one of the listeners in the small group stated with regret.

"Finding that your heroes, in fact, have feet of clay is the beginning of freedom. That's when you stand on your own feet and decide not to follow anyone," the sage explained.

Power

The CEO of a major business said one of his managers was highly competent and experienced but could not be promoted to any position involving power over people.

"Such a good man," he explained with regret, "but the moment he has access to that kind of power, it's as if a devil possesses him."

"Power is indeed a demon for someone who is not in a wise relationship with it," the sage concurred. "Power, like money, is something you can't possess without being possessed... unless you're awake."

Pretence

A film star told the sage he had achieved all his goals in his profession – fame, wealth and countless admirers – but he realised in the end that he did not know who he was. "In fact, I wonder if I have taken acting as a career or made acting my life. Either way, I have no peace."

"People invent many ways to avoid facing the truth of who they are," the sage commented. "Pretending to be who they are not, ignoring feelings that hurt, avoiding people who challenge them and never taking time to listen to themselves, are some of them. There is great peace in not having to pretend or act in real life."

Blindness

A visitor asked the sage about the human tendency to be blind to one's own faults.

"It's not only the difficulty in acknowledging one's own faults but also the quickness in finding them in others. People easily miss the elephant in their living rooms but would find a mouse in the neighbour's house," the sage said.

"I certainly see others differently from myself," the visitor agreed.

The sage continued, "It reminds me of the conjugation of irregular verbs: I am prudent, you are defensive, they are cowardly. I am persistent, you are stubborn, they are pigheaded."

Blind Spot

The newspapers reported the arrest of a kind and gentle philanthropist. The charges included major financial misappropriations, violence against his business partner and an attempt to murder his own wife.

Some of the visitors were incredulous. "How could such a man, known for a virtuous life and charitable works, do such things?"

The sage's simple comment was, "The bigger the front, the bigger the back."

Predictions

A retired school teacher noted that several of his students had belied his predictions about them. "I believed some of the well-behaved and studious young people had greatness waiting for them," he remembered. "And I was convinced that the troublesome ones who did not study well were doomed to fail. I was wrong in many instances."

He went on to cite the examples of a top industrialist in the country and a creative writer who were both students he had written off because of their behaviour when they were young.

"It's wonderful how education manages to miss putting out the light in so many of our students," was the sage's wry comment.

Emotions

Lesson

The sage was with some of his friends when he witnessed an old lady training her grandson for the trapeze. After the boy had made several unsuccessful bids to get over the bar, she said to him: "Son, just throw your heart over the bars, your body will surely follow."

The sage commented, "She's teaching a fundamental lesson about life: It's the heart that determines the direction of life."

Response

People who were in distress because of their struggles and problems would talk to the sage and find great peace. Hardened hearts seemed to melt and troubled ones were comforted.

"What is the secret of people's response?" asked a curious psychologist.

"I don't see people as good or bad but as free or stuck, happy or unhappy," the sage replied. "I don't judge or diagnose any one; I respond to their pain."

Contact

A visitor once wondered why so many human beings had difficulty getting in touch with their emotions but were quite liberal with their ideas and opinions.

"Describing our thoughts surely gives us a far wider conversational range than revealing our feelings," the sage observed.

Attention

A middle-aged man had come to take part in one of the sage's retreats, "I was just fine before I came to hear the sage. Now I'm disturbed. Why did you have to say things that upset people? I thought a retreat was supposed to make one feel good and nice."

The sage replied, "Your disturbance shows you what needs your attention. Be grateful that they surface so that you can see them. Unseen, they influence you anyway."

Empathy

One of the men who visited the sage was known in the
town to be aggressive and ruthless. His face was hard
and his voice harsh. After a few minutes of conversation, the
man's demeanour became calm and peaceful.

After he had left, one of the listeners asked the sage what the
secret of the change was. "It's the view from the heart," replied the
sage. "His harshness is the voice of his pain."

"But what about a man who creates troubles and causes sufferings
for other people?" the questioner continued.

"Look at them with your heart," the sage elaborated. "I've never
seen a troublesome man who isn't also troubled, or a man who
causes pain who hasn't been wounded first."

Disconnection

The sage would caution his listeners against the dangers of spirituality that is disconnected from the heart. He observed that people became rigid, cheerless and even heartless when spiritual practices were detached from their bodily and emotional life.

"Our feelings make us human, vulnerable and alive," he would tell them. "Listen to the heart – the hurts, fears, desires. When you so listen, your spirituality will be real."

Bliss

A man who visited the sage after a gap of two years said he was now a member of a group that practised a strict form of asceticism. They would seek, through rigorous practices, to obtain God's blessings.

"But there is no passion in your life. You have lost your aliveness and warmth. You have ended up as a spiritual refrigerator," the sage protested.

"But isn't it worth the price when the reward is the bliss of God?"

"Where is the bliss?" wondered the sage. "If your God were bliss, you wouldn't look like a sour puss."

Witnessing

Most visitors had ideas of how a spiritual person was supposed to think, feel and behave. They would expect him to be always available, ever friendly and generally placid. The sage, however, was full of life and would show his feelings. He was honest with people and would speak quite bluntly when necessary.

What baffled them sometimes was how he would be angry one moment and moments later he would be able to laugh and joke with the person he was angry with.

"Emotional states come and go and they are not personalised," the sage explained. "They are merely witnessed, so they have no chance to settle in me."

Courage

The sage was invited to a local rotary club meeting. In the course of their discussion someone praised the courage of a local hero who, risking his own life, had saved two girls from drowning.

"Isn't it great courage when you don't feel any fear and do something heroic?" one of the men asked, looking toward the sage for a response.

"Courage isn't the absence of fear," the sage replied. "You feel the fear and act in the moment, prepared to face the consequences."

"Aren't fear and courage in fact opposites?"

"They are opposites only when they are kept apart," the sage explained. "When awareness befriends fear, it becomes courage."

Fear

The former president of a bank that had collapsed said
the affairs of his bank were quite healthy and he had
believed that the financial crisis would leave it unscathed.

"I was wrong," the former banker said, "and the bank ended up
losing twenty-four billion dollars."

"How was that?" the sage asked.

"Bad debts bled us by four billion," the banker said. "Fear took the
rest."

Cultivation

A woman, angry about her husband's rudeness and insensitivity, said she had found great help in meditation, which helped her in cultivating gentleness.

"You can't fight one emotion with its opposite and hope to find peace. Your anger goes underground while you wear the mask of gentleness," the sage warned.

The woman was disappointed.

"The opposite contains the original," the sage continued.
"Go beyond this strategy and understand your anger.
Deal with it directly and deeply and you will find freedom."

Resentment

A woman said she was consumed with bitterness and resentment towards her ex-husband.

"I know I suffer from these feelings," she said, "but I must admit there is a part of me that wants to keep it that way to punish him."

"The hatred we have for another person indeed fashions a prison for us from which there is no parole. As long as we can't let go of thoughts of revenge and resentment, the heart is unfree and we suffer."

Grief

A man was heartbroken at the death of his wife. Within days he had put his house up for sale and moved to another town. He thought this would alleviate the grief.

"Geographical cures don't last," the sage pointed out. "You have to go back and deal with the grief."

"Does that mean I have to go back to the house I left behind? There was too much pain; everything there reminded me of her."

"Go back into your own heart. That's where the grief resides," the sage told the widower. "When your understanding frees you from grief, you will be free to live anywhere you want."

Limitation

A young man wanted to begin a new business venture.
He had the skills as well as the financial backing. "There is only
one obstacle," he told the sage. "My wife is against it. She is
terribly scared that I might fail and all will be lost."

"Have you done your homework and are you confident about
taking the risk?" the sage asked.

"I'm confident, but I'm uneasy about overriding her opinion," the
young man replied.

"If you want to be successful, you have to separate yourself from
other people's fears that limit you," the sage explained.

Company

A psychotherapist said that in her work with her clients, she would encourage cathartic expressions of emotions so they would experience some release. After several years of work, she noted that they kept going back to those feelings and getting stuck, not released. In fact, they seemed addicted to their unpleasant emotions.

"Are you surprised at your finding?" the sage asked. "We are known by the company we keep. If we stay with our fears, we become more fearful. If we dwell in our anger, we amplify it. We give power to what we keep going back to."

Clarity

A man said he was enraged by the poor quality of something he had purchased from a shop and had got into a fight with the manager. In fact, he was still angry and wanted to go back for another round.

"Strong emotions blind you and diminish your freedom. And the longer you carry them around, the more you suffer," the sage.

"That certainly is true," the man readily agreed. "Is there anything I can, in fact, do about the situation?"

"Do whatever you need to do to rectify the situation so that you are treated fairly. But before you can do that, you have to deal with your emotions so that you can see with clarity and act with purpose."

Power

A middle aged man said he was happy with his home and family. He was also earning a decent income. Unfortunately he had problems with two of his neighbours whom he described as selfish, unreasonable and difficult.

"When they were friendly, it was great," he said. "When they turned unpleasant, my feelings turned negative too."

The sage said, "That is what happens with a fine television when the remote control is in someone else's house."

Turmoil

A middle-aged woman said she had suffered considerable emotional turmoil in her life. Years of psychotherapy had only helped her marginally and she wanted to change.

"I keep thinking of the emotional problems of the past and the pain they have caused me," she said.

The sage asked her if she was keen on giving up her emotional problems. She was taken aback by the question.

"You seem to be looking for negative emotions like a swimmer who has a strange fascination for whirlpools," he said.

Stillness

Struggle

"It is a strange irony of life that people desperately look for happiness and struggle to find peace," the sage mused one day.

"That's the basic desire of all human beings, isn't it?" a friend asked.

"Of course it is," agreed the sage. "But we have to realise that it's readily available to us. To float in the water we have first to stop struggling."

Peace

During an informal conversation among friends, someone talked about a colleague of theirs who had been going through a series of painful experiences. They were astonished that in the midst of all that he was at peace.

"I guess he is in a state of denial," one of them commented. Most of them readily agreed.

"What if he is genuinely at peace?" said another friend.

"His peace may indeed be genuine," the sage joined in.

"How easy it is for us to be more comfortable with pain than joy, tears more than laughter, fear more than love! Cheerfulness in others is sometimes seen as just the suppression of hidden pain and optimism as delusion!"

Sharing

After listening to the sage speak about human suffering
and the possibility of experiencing peace and joy in life,
a visitor declared, "My unhappiness is my business alone. I don't
harm anyone with my misery. When I suffer, I suffer alone."

"Wrong," the sage disagreed. "You never suffer alone.
Everyone pays for your self-hatred and misery."

Restlessness

A successful businessman had spent endless hours at work, had rested little and had never taken a vacation. In the midst of a hectic schedule, he had acquired three major degrees in nine years, including a doctorate.

Now lonely, feeling lost and burnt out, he sought the sage with a question: "When will I find the peace that has eluded me all my life?"

The sage gave a short answer, "When you stop running."

Stimulation

"You speak about finding peace and stillness as necessary conditions for effective leadership," a business manager said. "I think some of us, in fact, thrive on conflicts."

"It's true, some are greatly stimulated by fighting," the sage replied. "However, once you've enjoyed a minimum level of peace within, you won't waste life energy on conflicts."

Terms

A stockbroker told the sage that he had been let down by some of his business associates and had suffered major losses.

"I tried to take revenge but they are even more prosperous now than before. I attempted suicide and I was rescued," he added.

After a brief discussion with him, the sage concluded, "Now that you have failed to dictate terms to life, you might as well accept the terms that life offers you. In that, you will find peace."

Quick-Fix

The sage steadfastly refused to offer programmes that appealed to people's greed, or promised to make them richer and more powerful. He would not endorse techniques that involved manipulating people or offering quick fixes for the problems of life without a deeper understanding.

Once a wealthy and admiring businessman proposed to pay phenomenal fees only if the sage would offer advice to his executives. "I know you have something that will benefit us greatly in these troubled times. It will help us tide over the awful economic problems we're facing if we follow your advice."

"In these turbulent times what you need is not more theories, advice or cleverness," the sage replied. "I can give you something that may really help. I can teach you to be silent, to be still in the midst of all the turmoil. There you will find wise answers and wholesome remedies."

The businessman looked at the sage sadly, unable to accept such an impractical piece of advice.

Refuge

A spiritual seeker engaged in real estate business had suffered major losses. He also gave time to community work where he had become the object of criticism. "How can I find some peace and quiet in the midst of all this?" he asked.

The sage listened to him with great concern. "My advice to you is this: Be an island unto yourself!"

"Does that mean I have to withdraw into isolation?"

"Far from it!" exclaimed the sage. "Surrounded by raging seas, beaten by powerful waves and swept by strong gales, you remain centred in the middle of it all."

Activity

"Human activity transforms the world," remarked a scientist.

"It is wholesome only when human stillness accompanies it," the sage noted. "Otherwise activity is harmful and even destructive."

The scientist was intrigued and asked him to explain further.

"Grasping hands are unable to give or receive. Restless eyes can't really see. Pounding hearts don't bring peace," the sage explained.

Pursuit

An intense looking young man said he had attained
nearly all the goals he had set for himself.

"I've exceeded my academic and professional goals," he said.
"Financial security and family life are the two remaining ones.
Once these two are reached, I'll find peace and quiet in life."

"Peace and joy in life are never attained through intense pursuit.
They are gifts that come to you when your struggle has ended,"
the sage cautioned him. "Cravings and silence never tread the
same path."

Civil War

At the end of a discussion about the conflicts and tensions that people encounter, a participant asked, "What in your experience is the root cause of our conflicts?"

"We're disturbed because we run away from who we are and try to become who we are not," the sage replied.

"We keep attempting to reach for what we can't get while ignoring what is always available. We'll find stillness only when this civil war has ended."

Battle

A man who returned from another course in mindfulness complained that the experience had been frustrating. "I wish to be like the others in the group who were able to be fully present there. My mind keeps wandering every time I try to stay focused, so there is no stillness."

"Shift your focus from battling with your mind and trying to subdue it," the sage suggested. "When your fears no longer control you and your desires no longer clamour for fulfilment, it is then that stillness comes."

Evasion

A busy software engineer who had wanted to find the wisdom of Awareness in stillness left his job and family and made off to the hills to spend his time alone. He hoped that one day he would become a teacher of awareness.

After a frustrating year he returned to consult the sage, who told him, "If you're seeking lasting stillness you have to find it in the business of life, work and family. In the hills you'll become a teacher only to the plants and rocks around you."

Balance

"I live an extremely busy professional life that has minimised my personal and family time," a visitor said. "I feel quite scattered in my life. I seem to be moving from one project to the next, hurtling from one problem to another. I make mistakes because I act impulsively. I'm often restless and frequently upset."

"A great mark of wisdom is the ability to distinguish between what is important and what is not," the sage replied. "Then you'll know when to act and when to be still, when to speak and when to be silent, which can bring balance to your life."

Laughter

A teacher talked to the sage about several difficult problems he faced at home as well as with his colleagues and students.

The sage suggested that he remain in silence imagining himself in those situations without taking himself too seriously.

The man paused for a few moments and then burst out laughing.

"If you're smart enough to laugh at the ironies of life," commented the sage, "you're certainly strong enough to face whatever comes."

Surrender

"Is there a sure and certain way to be always at peace?"
the sage was often asked.

"It's an open secret. If you wish to be at peace, you have to stop fighting what life brings."

"Does that mean that I wait passively for things to happen and not take action?"

"In every situation do whatever is necessary, yet know that the fruits of your actions are not yours to determine."

Non-Doing

A business leader spoke about the unprecedented upheaval in his organisation. He had tried to analyse the situation and apply the remedies suggested by experts, but they had not worked.

"Your stillness is the surest solution for your organisation's turmoil. So use your awareness as the most basic and reliable tool for your work," the sage responded.

"Perhaps I have to begin meditating," the businessman joked.

"Only choose one that involves seeing what is happening," the sage added. "You'll thus master the art of understanding deeply without analysing endlessly, and achieving much without doing a lot."

Presence

Solution

The head of a business firm talked about his hectic schedule, which left him little time for himself.

"I feel I'm often out of my depth, ending up confused and exhausted. When I need answers to some important problems, there is no one to turn to. Clearly there is no balance in my life."

The sage urged him to balance his activity with inner quiet. "Learn to listen to yourself deeply. In stillness is found a solution even to the most vexing problem. Everything is transformed by your presence to it."

Problem

"What is the quickest and surest way to change when a person is going through a problem?" asked a psychologist.

"By being present to it," the sage replied. "If you can be present to a problem with complete attention and intensity, without even the intention to change, you change."

Scholarship

Some of the sage's disciples believed that devotion to him would bring them enlightenment. They would miss no opportunity to be near him.

"There is no doubt that association with a sage is beneficial. But it's not magical, you have to translate that into action," advised the sage. "A goat reared in an ashram does not become a guru. A horse stabled on a university campus does not become a scholar. Nor does someone become a writer by drinking a lot of ink."

Motives

An artist who spent a lot of time in nature said he experienced a conflict between being present in nature and considering the artistic opportunities that nature offered. "It may be rather late in the day, but I realise that these have become obstacles to my presence."

"If you wish to be truly present, you have to be there without yourself," the sage said. "Go into nature, empty of motives and hopes of reward, your thoughts and your plans. For such a presence you have to go alone, without your ego."

Non-Possession

A woman said that after many struggles and heartbreaks she was finally happy. "I wish I could keep it this way and never lose it."

"Try not to possess it, only let it be present," the sage suggested.

"The shores don't own the ocean, nor the river banks the water that passes between them. Happiness is there in the moment, free of ownership and as delicate as a morning flower."

Experience

People were amazed at the power of the sage's words,
even his silence and presence. Asked about the secret
behind his ability to speak with such authority, the sage said,
"Awareness. Seeing with clarity."

When some of his listeners quizzed him about this reply,
he told them the story of a little girl who was asked by her family
on her first day at school about her experiences.

"'I was the prettiest child there,' she said

"The mother wanted to know, 'Who said so?'

"The little girl's reply was, 'Well, I was there. I could see.'"

Disclosure

"I came to the talk thinking you were going to talk about the divine presence in all things. Instead you talked about my being present to all things," an elderly man said.

"Experiencing your presence is more important than experiencing divine presence," the sage replied.

The man thought that was "over the top". "Here I am trying to get away from the sufferings in my miserable life and you bring me back to myself!" he complained.

"Attempting to experience divine presence is a cop out if it is at the cost of avoiding the truth of your life," the sage was quite blunt. "My work is to help disclose you to yourself, not to collude in your escape strategy."

Proximity

We're both doctors and married for 22 years. He does his thing and I do my thing, and there is freedom in that, which I thought was great," said a woman. "Until the shocking realisation hit me some days ago that we've been like two ships passing in the night; we really don't know each other."

"Proximity and tolerance are insufficient for love. You have lived next to each other, but you haven't been present to each other," said the sage. "Intimacy is your presence to another person free from needs and judgements."

Light

A journalist said he was being bullied and berated for an investigative article he had written. His friends and supporters had done little to support him and he felt all alone and had "fallen into a dark place where no light shines." He could see no way out of the darkness.

"You are most certainly hurting deeply and feeling abandoned in your time of need," the sage said. "But you must know that stars are always shining but we see them only in the dark. To see that, you have to be present even in your darkness."

Inside

"I have always tried to experience and live in God's presence," a religious woman said. "But I must admit that I find it difficult and frustrating. There is so much that distracts me all the time."

"If you attempt to experience God's presence outside that will remain a challenge," the sage replied. "If, instead, you experience that presence within you, you will soon realise there is no difference between outside and inside."

Impact

Among the sage's friends and acquaintances were celebrities, business tycoons and other wealthy people. However, his life was very simple and none of the glitter had entered his own home or life.

When someone asked why his life style remained unaffected, a disciple spoke: "When a rose is kept next to a diamond necklace, the rose doesn't shine, but the necklace may receive some of the perfume."

Happiness

Search

"I have searched for happiness my entire life," a middle-aged man told the sage. "I have looked everywhere, in wealth and pleasures, in intimacy and religion, in enjoyments and accomplishments."

Then with a sigh of disappointment he added, "Happiness is about the only thing that has eluded me in life."

"Happiness needs only a welcome, not pursuit" the sage commented. "Indeed it flees on being pursued but ensues when

Altruism

A young housewife told the sage that her life was not easy.
"When I got married, I resolved that I'd find my happiness and
fulfilment in making my husband and family happy."

The sage was quick to caution her. "Setting out to make other
people happy is a sure recipe for frustration and unhappiness.
Learn a basic lesson of life – it's not in your power to make
another human being happy."

Homecoming

A wealthy man said he had moved house twice that year looking for happier surroundings. He had moved from the city to the suburbs and finally to a more rural setting. He was still unhappy.

"Happiness is never found in moving to new homes but in coming home to yourself," the sage noted, "not in a change of address but in a change of attitude to life."

Solutions

There is so much that is wrong with the world," a spiritual teacher involved in social work noted. "Everywhere I look I see pain and problems. How can I be happy when there is so much suffering all around me?"

"You will never find peace and happiness in your life if the problems of the world have to be solved first," the sage replied. "Understand the difference between these two states: I'm happy because the world is all right and, the world is all right because I'm happy."

Renunciation

A businessman turned philanthropist was convinced that to find true happiness he had to renounce his wealth and leave home to live the rest of his life as a religious person.

The sage was not impressed. "If renunciation could guarantee peace and happiness, all monks and mendicants would be happy which, alas, is not the case," he observed. "Renunciation and sacrifice only breed conflict. Denial blocks the door to peace."

Contentment

A busy and ambitious businessman said, "I have always been driven to success and making money. When I achieve what I set out to do, there is always something more I desperately want to get. I can't seem to stop and find some peace and contentment in my life."

The sage was brief, "You'll find it when what you really want and what you truly need are exactly the same."

Opportunities

"I have a flourishing retail business: I have made tonnes of money, I have many powerful friends, and I'm still searching for something more," a visiting businesswoman said. "I thought regular contact with my guru would bring me the happiness I'm looking for. Even that has failed."

"Nothing in the world can make you happy," the sage observed. "Everything can offer opportunities and situations for you to be happy."

Selflessness

A social worker who was deeply involved in her work with the poor asked, "Isn't it selfish to seek your own happiness when there is so much suffering in this world? I try to find mine in my work for the poor."

"Seeking your own happiness is the most unselfish thing you can do in life. If you aren't happy yourself, you aren't going to make anyone else's life any happier," the sage replied. "It is the nature of happy people to share their happiness with other people; unhappy people likewise."

Obstacles

"What can I do to be happy?" a woman asked.

"Happiness is your natural state and there is nothing you can do to bring it on," the sage remarked. "The only thing to do would be to see the obstacles to happiness – your false beliefs, your clinging, and your demands that life must conform to your expectations."

Envy

"I must confess that I'm envious of people who have families intact, the security of a job, a good house and car, and enough money to spend," a visitor said. "I think these are the things that would give me the happiness that I'm lacking."

"Before you desire what others possess, it's always worth considering the happiness quotient of the people who own them," the sage commented.

Yearning

A young sportsman said he had the total love and support of his divorced mother throughout his life. She had earned money by cleaning people's houses.

"In spite of all my achievements I'm unhappy because I still don't have my father's love which is the one thing I have longed for all my life," he cried. "I've even been ashamed of my mother."

"Your mother's love, which you take for granted, doesn't make you happy and you yearn for the father's love that you can't gain," the sage observed. "You have all you need to be happy but you're like the vast majority of human beings who do not appreciate the near and pine for the far."

Desires

A wealthy businessman said that most of his goals have been attained in the twenty years he had been in business. "The gods have smiled on me and answered my prayers so far," he said. "I have just a few more desires to be fulfilled and I can be happy."

"Fulfilment of desires does not guarantee happiness," the sage replied. "The gods are only teasing you by answering your prayers and fulfilling your desires."

Position

A police officer who was close to retirement said he deserved promotion to the top post in his city but feared it might pass him by.

"I have long desired it and I may retire before my wish is fulfilled. This is one thing that could have ensured my happiness."

"If you are happy with yourself, you will not look for it in the posts and positions you long for," the sage said. "Positions never guarantee happiness. It is yours to bring happiness to the positions you hold."

Sympathy

A religious man recited a litany of sorrows – what others had done to him, the let downs and heart breaks. He had not found happiness in life.

"Give up your identity as a victim and sufferer if you wish to be happy," the sage told him. "Leave behind the war wounds and the marks of your crucifixion. These may bring you sympathy, but not happiness."

Contentment

A businessman said he had been upwardly mobile all his life. He had been successful but there was always something more that needed to be done. "I think I have come to a stage where I can end this tiresome pursuit of contentment and success," he said.

"I have a few more irons in the fire and once I get them, I'll be happy."

"If you are not content with what you have, you won't be content even if you get what you long for," the sage said. "The fulfilment of your desires is never the path to happiness."

Compensation

A woman who suffered major illnesses and family conflicts said, "I have suffered much. My hope is that for what I have gone through I'll be rewarded with some happiness now. I know there are no free lunches in life, everything comes at a price, even happiness."

"Happiness is not a reward for being unhappy or a compensation for misery," the sage said. "You have a good chance to be happy if you give up your mentality of struggle and your negative beliefs."

Disillusionment

A seeker said his disillusionment with religion had led him to various spiritual teachers. Finally he thought he'd found in the sage someone who held the secret, only to be disappointed with him too.

The sage laughed and said, "That's just as well. Otherwise you'd think you can find happiness outside yourself."

Result

"I have always led a rigidly austere life. I have prayed regularly. I can confidently say that I have followed the law scrupulously, yet I'm still unhappy and easily disturbed," a retired government official said with tears in his eyes.

The sage looked at him with compassion and said, "Happiness is not found in being moral, righteous or religious. In reality, genuine goodness, virtue and righteousness are the result of happiness, not the cause."

Prism

"I've suffered much in my life. My marriage was a calamity and ended in divorce. I trusted my business partner and he robbed me in broad daylight. I can't find honesty and trust anywhere, nor happiness," a visiting businessman said. "I'll be content to see if I can somehow bear with life and not hurt other people."

"When you're wounded, you tend to see everything through the eyes of your pain," the sage observed. "You have healed when you no longer see all things as damaged or that they can't be set right."

Sabotage

One day when the sage spoke about the strong beliefs of people that curtail or sabotage their happiness, a listener said, "I think I don't deserve to be happy or if I stumble upon it, sadness will follow, but I do want to be happy."

"That which you desire most is also what frightens you most," the sage commented. "If instead of some trickles of delight and crumbs of joy, you were to have a feast of happiness, would you who are accustomed to being a beggar, accept the invitation? If you were outrageously happy, could you handle it?"

Disengagement

A middle-aged man said he was frustrated with his family and friends. He felt let down by them in times of need. He thought he would isolate himself from people and live a quiet life with the hope of finding happiness alone.

"I no longer have the energy to make people happy or to do things for them, not even to work on relationships," he concluded.

"Disengaging from life because of frustrations and disappointments will never bring you happiness and peace," the sage advised. "You're like the sick person who cancels a doctor's appointment saying, 'I can't see you today, doctor, because I'm too sick!'"

Attitude

A successful doctor told the sage that he had chased happiness all his life and it was always in the next thing – professional success, marriage, family, finances, travels and so on.

"Though all these have given me great enjoyment, I haven't found happiness," he added. "Besides when some pleasant things happen, unpleasant events mar them and I'm just a plaything of events."

"Happiness is not found in the events that happen in life where pleasure and pain are like inseparable twins," the sage replied.

"Where is it then?"

"You will find lasting peace and happiness only in your attitude to all that happens, pleasant and unpleasant," the sage explained, "the attitude that enables you accept all that happens."

Threat

A friend of the sage once commented that many people in his society had considerable difficulty handling people who were free and happy.

"I don't understand why they have to subdue and control such people," he said.

"Happiness of another being is inexplicable to those who are unhappy," the sage said, "and the freedom of another is frightening to the fearful."

Regimentation

A sixty-year old man who looked thin and gaunt spoke to the sage slowly and with deliberation. "I can't claim to be happy but I have the satisfaction that I have pursued holiness by following the dictates of my conscience and the teachings of my religion. That has helped me to live a good life and do the right things."

"A life based on rules and teachings gets regimented and happiness is the first casualty. What is more important to you - being right or being happy, living an aware life or a moral life?" the sage said. "If you seek to live in freedom pursing neither happiness nor holiness, you would, in fact, be a whole lot happier. And genuinely holy, too."

About the Author

Dr. Francis Valloor is an author and international speaker. His life long quest brought him in contact with many wonderful spiritual teachers, friends and several masters and sages such as Anthony de Mello. It was he who set him on the path of Awareness. After de Mello's death, Francis worked as the director of Sadhana Institute in Lonavla, India for fourteen years before spending two years as a visiting scholar at the University of Notre Dame. Currently he lives in Dublin, Ireland where he works as a Clinical Psychologist in private practice and conducts Awareness workshops and retreats. He is the author of *A Dewdrop in the Ocean – Wisdom Stories for Turbulent Times* (2009) and *The Ocean in the Dewdrop – Awakening the Sage Within* (2010).

For more information, please visit: www.valloorinstitute.com

About the Artist

*The Cover artwork is a detail
of the painting ('The Alpha Awakening Spring / Oil on Canvas')
by renowned artist Paul McCloskey from Ireland.*

Paul McCloskey was born in Carrickmacross, Co. Monaghan and is now living and working in Gorey Co. Wexford. Paul attended the National College of Art and Design (N.C.A.D) Dublin and De Montfort University UK where he received a Masters Degree in Fine art painting (MFA) in 2010. He has exhibited extensively both nationally and internationally throughout the UK, London, Venice, Paris and New York and he has received multiple awards for his work, which are held in important collections.

*To learn more about Paul McCloskey and his work please visit
www.paulmccloskeyart.com*